SIPADAN

BORNEO'S UNDERWATER PARADISE

SIPADAN: Borneo's Underwater Paradise
First Published 1991 by Odyssey Publishing
Reprint 1994
27 Foch Rd, #05-01 Hoa Nam Building
Singapore 0820

Technical Editor: Prof. Chou Loke Ming Ph.D

Cataloguing-in-Publication data

Title: SIPADAN: Borneo's Underwater Paradise
Author: Michael P Wong

1. Marine life – Malaysia
2. Sipadan – Marine – Malaysia
3. Photography – Underwater
I. Wong M P   II. Title

ISBN: 981-00-2821-0

SIPADAN

BORNEO'S UNDERWATER PARADISE

Michael Patrick Wong

ACKNOWLEDGEMENTS

My sincere thanks and appreciation must go to the following organisations and people who helped with this book:

Datuk Joseph Pairin Kitingan,
Chief Minister,
The State of Sabah, Malaysia

Datuk Tan Kit Sher,
Minister of Tourism and Environment Development,
Sabah, Malaysia

Datuk Wilfred Lingham,
Permanent Secretary, Ministry of Tourism and
Environmental Development,
Sabah, Malaysia

Prof. Chou Loke Ming,
Reef Ecology Study Team, Dept of Zoology,
National University of Singapore
(Technical Editor)

Prof. Jennifer George,
School of Biological and Health Sciences,
Polytechnic of Central London

Dr. David George,
Natural History Museum,
London

Dr. Jeanne A Mortimer,
World Wide Fund for Nature,
Malaysia

Dr. Elizabeth Wood,
Consultant Marine Biologist,
London

Ron Holland,
Directors and staff of Borneo Divers and
Sea Sports (Sabah) Sdn Bhd

Malaysian Airline System Berhad
(Kuala Lumpur)

Fred Siems,
Malaysian Airline System
(New York)

Sabah Air Pte Ltd

Christopher Lim

Freddy Ee

Lawson Wood

J K Jeyakumar

Equipment
Underwater photographs were taken using Pentax LX SLR cameras, with lenses ranging from 16mm to 100mm macro. They were placed in Hugyfot underwater housings constructed by René Hugenschmidt of Switzerland.

Sea and Sea YS 200 strobe units were used to light the subjects. In strong currents the Nikonos II and III with 20mm or 15mm lenses were used.

Film used was by Fuji, either RF50 or Velvia.

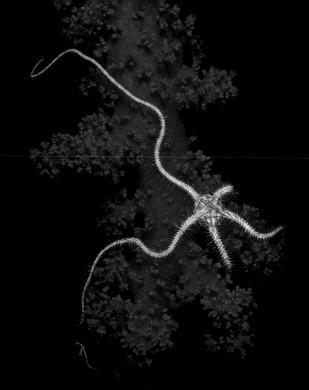

For my wife, Suzzana and my sons, Louis, Cedric and Leon

PREFACE

*T*his beautiful book that attempts to feature the wonders of Pulau Sipadan will take readers to some of the most treasured and spectacular underwater sights that have made this island famous for worldwide.

Sabah is indeed honoured that the national airline, Malaysia Airlines, has undertaken this publication to promote the wonders of Pulau Sipadan. We are grateful for Mr. Michael Wong's skilful and attractive photographic portrayal of the island.

I am hopeful that the publication of this book will spotlight Pulau Sipadan both locally and abroad and further promote it as a tourist destination. However, whilst the State Government has placed priority on tourism development, we will also make great efforts to curb exploitation of the environment and destruction of the state's natural attractions. Pulau Sipadan and many of Sabah's natural heritage must be protected and preserved.

I am confident that this book will do much not only to promote Pulau Sipadan but also to introduce Sabah to the outside world. This 'Land Below the Wind' coupled with the warmth of its people and many natural wonders from the majestic Mt. Kinabalu to the colourful splendour of its flora and fauna will not fail to captivate visitors to the state.

I wish to congratulate Malaysia Airlines and Mr. Michael Wong for their splendid efforts.

(Tan Sri Datuk Haji Sakaran Dadai) PSM, SPDK, PGDK, ADK, JP
Chief Minister of Sabah

*M*alaysia is blessed with a diverse natural heritage which ranges from the most spectacular Marine Park in the world to the oldest Tropical Rainforest.

While in its pristine state, we must protect and preserve these priceless treasures for the future generations.

Malaysia Airlines takes great pride in contributing towards this cause.

And to raise awareness of the importance of conservation, we are promoting eco-tourism.

For these reasons, we support and applaud Michael Wong's effort to place Malaysia in the map of the world's best diving spots.

To quote Jacques Cousteau, 'Sipadan is an untouched piece of art.'

The photographs in this award-winning book testify to that. It opens up a world seen only by the few.

Even more impressive is the fact that many of Sipadan's inhabitants are unique to this island towering 2000 feet above the ocean floor.

As a documentary, it brings us closer to understanding marine life, and in the process, a deeper appreciation of nature.

For naturalists, environmentalists, adventure-seekers or simply, the curious this book should put Sipadan high on the wish list.

We invite you to explore one of the many wonders of Malaysia.

CONTENTS

INTRODUCTION

*A*lone in a wide expanse of sea, Pulau Sipadan hides its secret well. Viewed from the deck of an approaching boat, it could hardly look more ordinary. Yet, encircling this tiny enforested island is a coral reef, one of a kind, unique.

Lying a 45-minute speedboat trip off the northeast coast of the island of Borneo in the state of Sabah, East Malaysia, Pulau Sipadan looks like any one of a thousand other coral isles in the tropics. Only four hectares in size, this island lies low in cool blue water with broad leafed trees reminiscent of primary jungle and sandy beaches; it is idyllic and very romantic.

But it is not the romanticism of a tropical isle which draws me back to Sipadan (Pulau means island in the Malay language) twice each year since 1988. Nor is it the fact that I was born and lived in Borneo until my teens. It is the secret underwater paradise of Sipadan which has me enthralled, and keeps pulling me back.

Having dived a range of the world's most renowned reef sites, I can say without hesitation that Sipadan has to be one of the most pristine and exquisite reefs on which it has ever been my privilege to dive. On each visit the compulsion to get underwater is always irresistible.

There is very little of a holiday about my visits to Sipadan. The preparation for each trip starts more than a month before departure, with final equipment checks in a London swimming pool and the inevitable last minute servicing.

Back-up units of my favourite lenses and strobes, with their various chargers, all require scrutiny and checking against the equipment inventory list. Batteries are fully charged, cameras are assembled and everything duly packed into their special shipping cases, without forgetting the tiny screwdrivers and all of the other items essential to a successful photo assignment.

The actual journey starts with an excess baggage charge at London Heathrow. However, after three years of frequent flying, airlines have given a special dispensation.

The long haul from London is followed by a brief stop over in Singapore to stock up with film and collect my serviced dive gear. A quick hop to Sabah's capital, Kota Kinabalu, to collect the rest of my gear from storage, a short flight to Tawau, a transfer to a coach for a two-hour drive, and finally at Semporna, catch the speedboat for the island. I arrive on Pulau Sipadan a total of 18 travelling hours after leaving London.

Pulau Sipadan lies 35 kilometres or 45 minutes by speedboat off the coast of Semporna - alone in the wide expanse of sea.

On arrival I am ready and prepared to head straight for the water within the hour. It takes very little time to register for my thirty day stay, catch up with old acquaintances and unpack before I am clambering into my dive gear ready for the spectacle below.

The first dive of the trip sets the fanatical routine which sees me spending up to eight hours each day in the water. I try to make it a rule that the first dive of each day must be deep, to then work my way gradually to the surface. All subsequent work must take place in the shallower depths. This prevents nitrogen building up in the bloodstream.

I always try to avoid decompression diving, paying very close attention to my dive computer and monitoring it constantly. Without strict attention to the computer's calculations, a build-up of nitrogen gas could result in the bends, dreaded by all divers.

On reaching land again, I immerse my cameras' protective waterproof housing in fresh water to wash off the accumulated salt. After soaking and drying they must be cleaned and the seal greased, before the reloaded cameras can be placed back in the waterproof casings. Flooding of the camera housing can ruin a camera; the slightest piece of corrosion dirt or dust trapped in the rubber seal can allow water to seep inside the casing. These casings are checked and re-sealed ready for action. Only then do I allow myself a cup of tea and a snack before returning to the water's shallow depths.

Once the pattern has been set on the first day the regimen and the pace remain as gruelling for the entire thirty day period.

On every visit my underwater cameras and I are inseparable, and at the end of the day each is as exhausted as the other. A picture is said to be worth a thousand words, but I doubt if a thousand pictures could do justice to this oceanic realm.

Yet, with the photographs in this book I hope to convey something of the excitement, variety and colour of the Sipadan reef. These few pages of text merely provide an insight into the origins and natural history of the island and its reef.

Right: Underwater locations at Sipadan named by Ron Holland of Borneo Divers Sdn Bhd.

A LONELY PINNACLE OF ROCK

As the largest island in the archipelago which separates the South China Sea and the Pacific Ocean, Borneo sits astride the equator and is politically divided into four areas: The Indonesian province of Kalimantan, the autonomous Sultanate of Brunei Darussalam, and the federated Malaysian states of Sarawak to the south and Sabah in the north. Sipadan is 5° north of the equator, and administratively belongs to Sabah.

Very few maps are detailed enough to mark Sipadan's position. Even those charts which do indicate the position seldom reveal the feature which makes it so unique.

As the only deep water oceanic island in Malaysia, the island itself is the tip of a precipitous seamountain; an isolated column of rock rising defiantly from the sea floor about six to seven hundred metres below. Other Malaysian islands rest on the shallow seabed of the Continental Shelf, generally at depths less than a hundred metres.

Sipadan is perched on the northern margin of the Sulawesi Sea, a huge basin, which at its deepest point plunges to 6,200 metres. On the island's landward side, it is separated from the edge of the Continental Shelf by a trough 1,000 metres deep, while on the seaward side the reef drops off dramatically in a 2,000 metre contour. The living reef occupies only the top fifty metres of the mount. Its profile and other characteristics are greatly influenced by the deep and awe-inspiring sea wall of living coral.

VOLCANIC ORIGINS

Sipadan was formed as an undersea volcano millions of years ago during the Pliocene and Quaternary periods of enormous

West Ridge

Hanging Gardens

Lobster Lairs

Turtle Beach

Jetty/Drop Off

Lighthouse

Dive Centre

Turtle Cavern/Tomb

Barracuda Point

Staghorn Crest

Coral Gardens

South Point

White Tip Avenue

Midreef

Turtle Patch

N

volcanic activity. A period which also saw the creation of the Semporna Peninsula on the Borneo mainland.

According to government reports, it is unlikely the volcano which forms Sipadan's core ever extended above sea level, although, it must have come very close to the surface to enable a fringing coral reef to have formed around the peak. Over time, probably during the Quaternary period, fluctuations in the sea level of as much as 150 metres caused a coral atoll to be formed. This atoll comprised a ring of coral reef whose outermost edge was covered by a very thin layer of live coral polyps – all generating calcium carbonate to sustain their chalky skeletons.

As the sea waves pounded the reef, pieces of coral limestone were broken off and washed towards the central lagoon. As time passed, the centre of the atoll filled with sand. Eventually either a lowering of the sea level or a tectonic uplifting (or perhaps a combination of the two) probably caused the island to emerge from the surface of the sea.

The presence of underwater limestone caves provides clues suggesting a more complicated geological history. These caves contain stalactites and flowstone. Stalactites cannot form underwater since they are the result of water seeping through rock surface and dripping into a dry cavern. So these formations indicate that about 20,000 years ago, during the last major period of glaciation, a dramatic reduction in the sea level left Sipadan high and dry as a coral limestone island.

There is also other evidence that the elevation of Sipadan was once much higher above sea level than it is today. At depths of about thirty metres there are ledges running along the reef. Although they have yet to be surveyed, they may well prove to be wave-eroded platforms from a bygone era.

As divers we see only the limestone cap, and not the volcanic rock beneath which forms the base and part of the stem of the seamount.

Top: A diver approaches the vast entrance to the limestone cave system.

Above: Inside the caverns stalactites and flowstone formations are an impressive feature.

THE LIVING REEF

A coral reef is not just rock but a collection of living organisms, comprising millions of tiny creatures. Just by looking at the reef as it is tells us something of the forces which have shaped it over the years, and of the changes which are still acting on it.

While the reef's north-south orientation is probably connected with the shape of the underlying rocky pinnacle, it also emphasizes the fact that corals are living creatures which respond to their environment. In these latitudes, prevailing monsoon winds blow alternately from the north-east (November to March) and the south-west (May to September). Where waves sweep in, corals reach out to meet them, flourishing in the fresh, food-rich water. As a result the reef has taken on an asymmetrical shape. Even so, it is not a static structure but one that changes and constantly adapts.

Behind the scenes, a battle is going on between coral growth and erosion. The surge and flow of tidal currents encourage coral growth, but also wears away coral limestone deposits. Under these conditions reefs grow, forming huge buttresses intersected by surge channels. Such underwater scenery is typical along parts of the Sipadan reef. In places especially along the north side of the island, the channels are almost vertical sand chutes. Off the south of the island in deeper waters are majestic gullies paved with corals.

A dramatic feature of Sipadan's underwater paradise is the precipitous reef wall for which the island has become justifiably famous amongst the small band of divers who have visited the island. At one point, on the northern end of the island, the drop-off is only a few metres from the shore and falls almost vertically into the deep. Its position is marked by an abrupt change in water colour from pale green on the shallow beach-side, to an intense dark blue where the seabed is hundreds of metres down.

Top: Close-up of the reef at Barracuda Point.

Above: Just a few metres from the shoreline, the shallow gives way to a sudden precipitous 600 metre wall, The Drop Off.

Top: Gorgonians, or sea fans, effectively filter water to extract food particles. The individual polyps trap particles with ease, when fully extended.

Above: Commonly known as bigeyes, this solitary Priacanthus seeks refuge beneath the shade of a table Acropora. Similar to the squirrel and soldier fishes, the Priacanthus is nocturnal and spends the daylight hours in caves and dark crevices. It preys on other small fish, crustaceans and cephalopods.

UNDERWATER EXPLORATION

The main problem of conveying the majesty of the Sipadan reef photographically is knowing where to begin. Every visitor to this reef takes away particular personal recollections; their own favourite scenes imprinted in their minds.

I came away with a host of memories. It was only later, after viewing more than 21,600 slides, the result of more than 600 rolls of film and more than 1,200 underwater hours of photographic work, that it occurred to me the most logical place to start was with the coral crust. Were it not for the hard corals there would be no island, no submarine walls festooned with marine life, no turtles, or vast shoals of fish.

Corals grow best in clean, clear water and thrive at Sipadan. They come in many shapes and colours, from bluish branching colonies to brown plates, orange cup corals and the black coral, highly prized by the jewelry industry.

The coral is a simple creature, yet it is the only animal capable of building giant geological formations which can be seen by satellites. Corals also provide a complex habitat for a fascinating range of other animals and plants.

Providing spectacular underwater scenery, some soft coral species have the ability to expand and contract according to the tidal ebb and flow. During an explorative dive, separated from my "buddy", I was astounded by a 2-metre tall, soft coral waving in the current. Having taken its bearing I returned the following day to photograph it with a colleague in the frame to give an idea of its scale. Try as we might we just couldn't find it!

During a subsequent dive we found a shorter version of my gigantic find, later still, according to the current's flow, the same coral had extended almost to full size. On investigation I discovered that with incoming tide the creature inflates itself with water to present the maximum feeding surface. At slack current periods it expels inflationary water to return to the sea bed as a small insignificant clump of yellow animal matter.

FISH IN ABUNDANCE

The fish at Sipadan are truly spectacular. A whole aquarium of brightly coloured fish cruise around steep slopes, stand guard in caves, loiter on the sea floor and cluster around corals. Many of the species which live here are only very rarely seen on other Malaysian reefs and some are exclusive to Sipadan. It is the island's position, in deep water far from land, which attracts the big oceanic species, while the precipitous cliffs and other coral areas provide suitable habitats for many other varieties.

Off the reef face, shoals of fusiliers, snappers, surgeon fish and caranx stream past, creating brilliant swirling patterns against the clear, blue water beyond. In their midst are bizarre-looking unicornfish, distinguished by their long horn. No less strange are the bulging heads of the humphead parrot fish which sometimes gather in aggregations of over fifty individuals. They are an impressive sight as they lunge at the coral, aggressively biting off fist-sized chunks.

It is not unusual to have close encounters with literally thousands of large barracuda. Often the massive schools congregate to give an awesome display; circling and moving like an underwater tornado. The ultimate thrill for a diver is to penetrate the eye of the tornado and be surrounded by a moving mass of metre-long fish.

On one occasion, I was "buddy diving" with a colleague when we came across a shoal of these barracuda circling. My "buddy" was working with his video camera, while I was shooting with my Pentax. He signalled to me that he was going into the epicentre. I followed, shooting upwards from below him, with the sunlight glinting through the wall of fish from the surface above.

Once inside the tornado, the sound generated by the movement of the barracuda was like a low frequency hum of a generator or electric razor. At times the circle tightened so that he was just an arm's reach from the barracuda.

Below: Sphyraena barracuda, curious by nature, sometimes follows divers, making them feel uneasy. Individuals of this species can grow to two metres in length.

Bottom: The bigeye trevally, Caranx sexfasciatus, distinguished by a white tip on the dorsal fin lobe, hunts in schools. Juveniles can occasionally be found in rivers and estuaries.

Nightly, Green Turtles come up onto the beach to lay eggs. Having hatched as a community, the baby turtles immediately scamper to the water. This is the point where the baby turtles are genetically imprinted to return to the same beach to lay their own eggs in later years.

It was an exhilarating but intimidating experience. The popular misconception is that barracuda are aggressive when aroused, but there we were, in the centre of thousands of these docile creatures, the light blocked out by a swirling wall of fish.

But this display did not last long. After 15 minutes, the school broke up and swam away apparently in search of richer feeding grounds.

On a morning dive off Barracuda Point, I came across a shoal of more than twenty hammerhead sharks. Sharks are no strangers to divers who accept them as part of the territory and hazards of diving. However, twenty hammerheads shoaling was a rare encounter indeed.

TURTLE ODYSSEY

Possibly my favourite sea creature is the turtle. Sipadan is unusual in that it is the only island in Malaysia where divers can expect to encounter a large number of turtles. Two main species, the Hawksbill and the Green turtle, can be found in Sipadan's waters.

A protected species, the Hawksbill turtle can be found on rocky shorelines, coral reefs and lagoons throughout much of Malaysia. Despite its small carapace length of a maximum of ninety centimetres, the Hawksbill can lay more eggs on average than any other turtle, approximately 150 per nest.

The Hawksbill is an omnivorous species that obtains its food primarily from the reef environment. Its sharp 'hawks-bill' beak is particularly adapted to extracting food items from coral crevices and cavities. Its favourite food is the sponge. The Hawksbill is one of a few animals known to feed on sponges, as a result it keeps a check on the growth of sponge species which might otherwise become too abundant.

The Green turtle is also a protected species. It is migratory, and widely distributed throughout the tropical, and sub-tropical regions.

Preferring undisturbed beaches and overhanging branches under which to nest, the green turtle lays an average of 100-120 eggs per nest and usually nests about five times during each breeding season. Individual turtles only come to nest once every two to five (or more) years.

A herbivorous species, the Green turtle will swim thousands of kilometres from its nesting beach to feed on seagrass or algae beds.

In the caverns at the northern end of the island, the eerie sight of turtle skeletons is unforgettable. Sentimentalists may choose to believe that the turtles seek out caves as a final resting place, a sort of turtle variation on the African legend of the elephant's graveyard. The reality, however, is much sadder.

It is almost certainly by accident rather than by design that the turtles end their lives in the dark of the limestone caverns. Entering the caverns perhaps to rest, the poor creatures become lost in the labyrinth of tunnels and caves. Disorientated and cut off from the surface and source of air, they inevitably drown.

The floor of the flooded cave, known locally as Turtle Tomb, is littered with skeletons of those that have perished, with ancient ones buried deep in the fine silt. Sometimes a recent victim is found floating against the ceiling, its body inflated with gases that have built up as its flesh decomposes. Feeding on this carrion are thousands of shrimps and minute transparent crabs. As the body disintegrates the remains fall to the cave floor, providing food for numerous large worms playing a further significant part in the cycle of regeneration.

Not everything in the caverns is connected with this cycle of death and decay, but even so the dark interior is not an easy place to live, the only visible inhabitants are schools of flashlight fish. It is only back towards the entrances that things really start to come to life again, and only when you emerge on into the sea once more can the diver savour again the glorious colours of the outer reef.

Below: Diagram of Turtle Tomb (not to scale) which lies directly under huts 14 and 15. (From sketches provided by Ron Holland).

Bottom: Skeletal remains of a turtle found in Turtle Tomb.

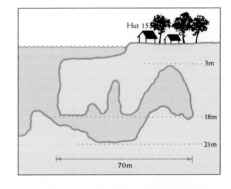

21

ISLAND WILDLIFE

Idle moments between dives provide an opportunity to explore the island. Despite its small size there is much interest, mainly because it has remained undisturbed for so many years. Virtually every night of the year especially from August to October, turtles haul up on to the beach to lay their eggs in the soft sand. They are not the only reptiles to make use of the island in this way; the amphibious sea snake does exactly the same, seeking a sheltered spot for its eggs beneath stones and vegetation at the top of the beach near the tree line.

Small lizards abound, the lucky visitor will get a glimpse of giant water monitors which swim or run with equal agility. Also rustling about in the undergrowth are robber or coconut crabs. The largest of the land crabs, which is a modified form of hermit crab, has become rare in many parts of the tropics due to disturbance and over-exploitation. Sipadan is the only spot in Malaysia where the robber crab can be found.

The compact and luxuriant rain forest contains all manner of exotic plants and animals. Huge hardwood trees towering thirty to forty metres above the forest floor

Top: The migratory pied imperial pigeon, Ducula bicolos.

Above: Sipadan was originally designated as a bird sanctuary.

provide roosting for more than forty-seven species of birds, while in the dense undergrowth below is a great variety of insects and other small animals. Flowering fig trees perfume the air, attracting fruit bats which fill the night with their chattering as they feed hungrily on the sweet offerings.

Top: Monitor lizards inhabit the shoreline. This specimen, called Morris, often raids the resort rubbish dump.

Above: Coconut crabs are indigenous to Sipadan.

Left: Bayan tree.

SIPADAN'S PAST

Protected by its distance from the mainland and its lack of safe anchorage, Sipadan has remained a natural paradise. Local superstition also holds that in a sink hole in the centre of the island, there lurks a giant octopus. Its lair, apparently, is connected to the outside by a labyrinth, like the underwater cave system.

Legend has it that the carnivorous octopus comes out to devour humans. Where that particular story originated is unclear. But a combination of superstition, remoteness, and fear of sea pirates, has ensured that the island has never been properly colonised by humans, until recently.

In the past, it was not the splendour of the reefs that drew people to visit, but the turtle eggs in the sand and a plentiful supply of fish in the sea. Its fame as a turtle breeding island has been known for at least fifty years. Local stories tell that the inhabitants of an island to the north, Pulau Dinawan, were the first to collect turtle eggs from Sipadan on a regular basis. Since turtle eggs are a highly prized delicacy in South East Asia, they used them as part of a rent paid to their landlord, the Sultan of Sulu. These long-established collection rights have been maintained amongst local people.

Naturalists first became interested in Sipadan in 1933 but this was on account of the bird population rather than the marine life. At that time the island was declared a bird sanctuary specifically to protect the rare Nicobar Pigeon species. The first dives and marine studies were not carried out until the late 1970's, and there is still much to be discovered.

Possibly the last of Sipidan's traditional turtle egg collectors. The rod he carries is used to probe the sand to find the turtle nests.

THE FUTURE

The photographs in this book are an attempt to capture the range and variety of Sipadan's underwater life as it is today, in 1991. What will it look like by the year 2,000? Could danger lie in that the very richness of the underwater paradise which makes it so appealing to the diving public also lead to its decline?

A decade ago the island was not a tourist destination. Except for the turtle egg collectors and occasional fishermen, Sipadan's beaches were deserted and the reefs remained undisturbed.

But now that the fame of Sipadan has spread throughout the diving community, it is not enough to simply hope that the unique environment will escape unscathed. Such hopes have been sadly dashed at other reef sites throughout the world. Seldom is the damage inflicted intentionally, often it disintegrates little by little. With the increase in the number of visitors and the infrastructure which supports them, more and more pressure is placed on the environment.

Coral takes years to grow, forming the framework of the reef. This evolutionary process can be broken in an instant by the careless sweep of a diver's fin or the impact of a boat's anchor. The most experienced,

At the Drop Off, local fishermen in their pump boats.

Robber crabs do not only use shells for housing.

sensitive divers with the utmost care can also damage corals simply by inadvertently brushing up against them.

In the same way, visitors meaning no harm may, with their noise and bright lights, frighten away turtles which come to nest on the island's beaches. Already large numbers of eggs are harvested for food. According to some scientific theories, female turtles make a habit of returning to the same beach from which they hatched and it would be a high price to pay if the adults were driven away from their nesting ground permanently.

There is pressure for space to build accommodation, and the small reservoir of freshwater available on the island is taxed to the limit. If vegetation is cut back, or has to compete with visitors for fresh water, the sandy surface of the island can be exposed leading to serious erosion. Litter and sewage left by the new colonist, man, has to be dealt with in a way that will ensure that the environment does not suffer.

On the other hand it should theoretically be easier to keep a careful watch on what happens to such a small and isolated site, and to prevent damage from occurring.

There has to be a compromise between making this pristine natural spectacle available for the appreciation of visitors, and the preservation of the island's delicate ecosystem. Truly, I hope this can be achieved.

A living organism, the reef reaches out into the current to absorb and be nourished by the food-rich water.

The undersea creatures which inhabit the reef are often echoes of a distant pre-historic past — locked into the present age, but primitive in their origins these throwbacks abound.

Perfectly adapted to their environment, hard and soft coral, gigantic sea fans, countless varieties of sea-squirts form a glorious garden of colour and life, covering the top fifty metres of the seamount which is Sipadan.

Preceding page: The reef top showing prolific growth of the hard coral, Acropora *and bushes of the soft coral,* Litophyton. *Numerous small fish such as the blue* Chromis *and orange females and purple males of the fairy basslet* Pseudanthias squamippinus *are common here.*

Above: Covering a large part of the reef is a bed of lettuce coral, Montipora, *while in the foreground is a small patch of branching* Acropora.

Right: Dominating this part of the reef are large colonies of branching Acropora *which provide a habitat for a wide variety of fish and invertebrates, such as the fan worm. As one of the fastest growing forms of coral the* Acropora *can survive very turbulent waters.*

Left: At Mid Reef, at a depth of 45 metres, the soft coral, Dendronephthya, grows in tree-like formations which can often dwarf divers to reach heights of over two metres when fully extended.

Right: During the slack current periods the colony contracts and the feeding polyps appear as clusters with protruding calcareous spicules. With the increase of the current, this species inflates to form an erect fan providing a greater feeding surface area.

36

Above: The spectacular soft coral, Dendronephthya, *suggested the name of this spot, Hanging Garden.*
When feeding, they appear to be in full bloom. While when the current is slack they droop, like ferns (left).

Far left: Detail of the Dendronephthya *coral, which displays a variety of shades.*

Left: The large melithaeid sea fan with its plant-like growth is firmly attached to the reef by a tuft of branches which contains a central strengthening rod of horny material (gorgonin).

Below: The sea fan orients itself at right angles to the current presenting the maximum feeding surface.

Above: The striking white feeding polyps of the sea fan, Siphonogorgia, contrast strongly with its red branches.

Right: Melithaeid sea fan at a depth of approximately 50 metres at Barracuda Point.

Far right: The characteristic sea fan, Subergorgia hicksoni, can reach heights of over one metre and is frequently found on deep wave-exposed reef fronts.

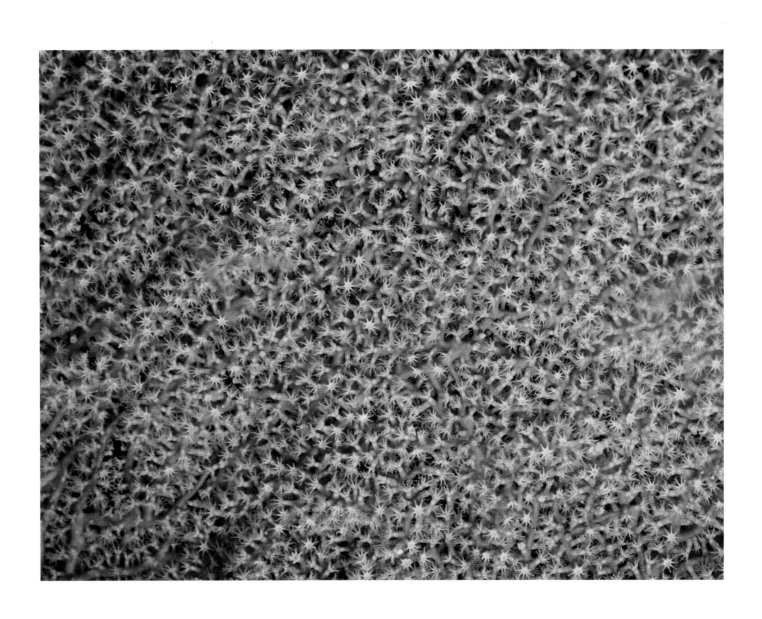

Above: The feeding polyps and bright red branches of Siphonogorgia, *a sea fan, display a flowing pattern.*

Left: The density of the polyps on the branches of the gorgonian sea fan creates interesting red and yellow patterns presenting a formidable feeding area.

When photographed with a macro lens most reef creatures display a fascinating range of shapes, colours and patterns.

Below: The pink tipped tentacles of the large Sea Anemone, Entsemaea quadricolor, contain poisonous stinging cells to kill its prey.

Right: The Fungia coral is easily recognisable on the reef by its distinctive pattern of sharp ridges reminiscent of an upturned mushroom hence its common name, Mushroom Coral.

Right: Polyps of the soft coral, Sinularia, *with fully extended tentacles ready to trap plankton.*

Right, below: The occulinid coral, Galaxea astreata, *has an intricate structure which gives it a distinctive appearance.*

Far right, above: The very spiny texture of this mussid coral, Acanthastrea echinata, *makes it easily recognisable on the reef.*

Far right, below: Marked by a pattern of long wavy valleys and ridges, the beauty of Platygyra daedalea, *a faviid coral is further enhanced by its strong, contrasting colour scheme.*

Above: The tubular polyps of the coral Favia *forms a mosaic of green over the reef.*

Left: A cluster of kidney shaped tentacles from the hard coral Euphyllia ancora.

Left: At White Tip Avenue, an isolated gorgonian colony of Echinogorgia *stands like a sentinel guarding one of the reef's spectacular passages.*

Above: The bizarre tightly-coiled whip coral, Cirrhipathes spiralis, *grows horizontally from the steep reef slopes at depths below 20 metres.*

Right: At West Ridge, large bushes of the black coral Antipathes *grow on reef ledges in the deeper areas and are frequently used as substratum by the winged mussel,* Pteria.

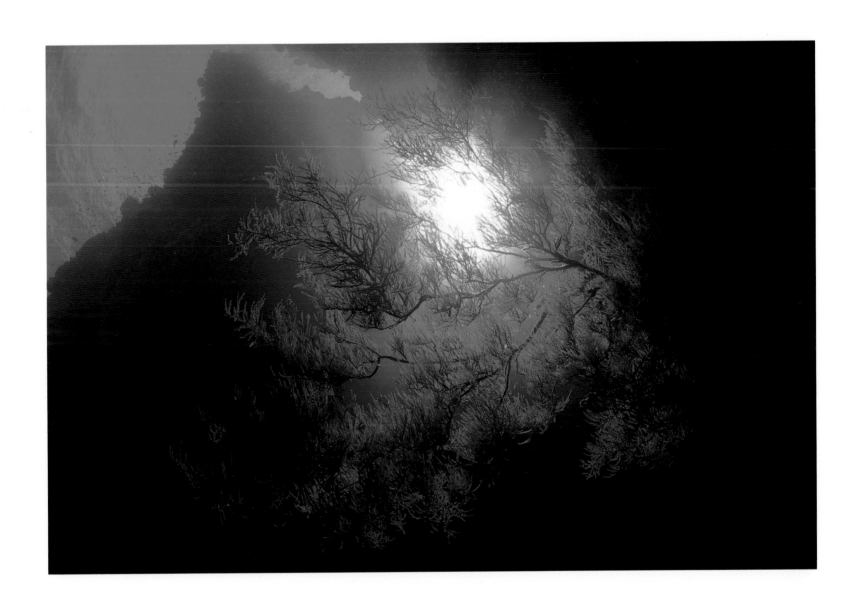

Left: Huge barrel sponges, Petrosia sp., over two metres in height can be found in the darker depths at around 65 metres at Barracuda Point. The sponges can often provide a habitat for other creatures, such as the calcareous tube worm.

Far left: The encrusting growths of other organisms contribute to the colourful pattern of the double-barrelled sponge, Xestospongia.

Right and below: Underwater coral and sponges can often take surprising shapes. Here two sponges grimace for the camera.

Far right: Sponges come in a wide variety of forms and colours. At South Point the red sponge, Latrunculia corticata, branches out of the reef .

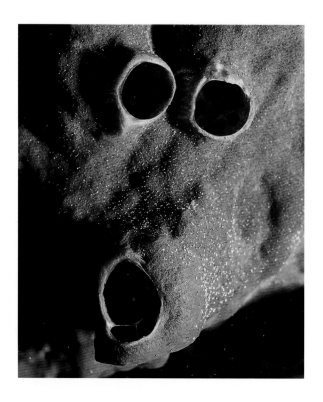

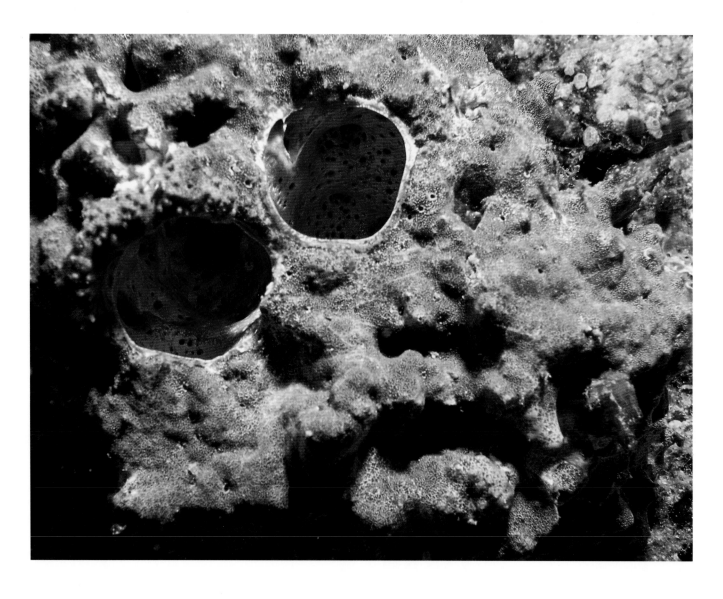

Left: The sponge's habit of over-growing other living organisms, especially sea fans, often leads to complex branching. This sponge appears to be hanging from the steep reef wall by just a thread.

Right: The abnormal growth of this sponge can possibly be attributed to the result of earlier damage caused by a predator.

Below: During daylight hours, the large smooth tubes of the sponge, Siphonochalina, provide safe havens for small crabs and shrimps.

Above: Seldom to be found in large
numbers, the bright blue sea squirt,
Rhopalaea crassa, *with its
golden rim inhabits both shallow
and steep reefs throughout Asia,
from the Western Indian Ocean
to Japan.*

Right: The conspicuous green sea
squirt, Didemnum molle, *a
common Indo-Pacific species.*

Left and below: Sea squirts can often be found with a covering of brightly coloured sponges. When the sea squirt is disturbed, it closes the water intake opening at the top for protection.

Right: In macro-view the sea squirt, Polycarpa aurata, shows its thick tough leathery tunic and large siphons. When feeding, a current of water containing food particles enters the sea-squirt through the top siphon and is expelled from a valve half way down the body.

Right, below: A view down the inhalant siphon of a transparent sea squirt showing the food-filtering device, the branchial basket.

Left: The soft coral expands its delicate feeding polyps at night to reveal transparent walls through which can be seen the creature's internal structure. The feathery tentacles contain stinging cells which catch small organisms swimming past.

Below: The extended food trapping tentacles of the sabellid fan worm contain small eyes which react like photo-electric cells. The shadow of a predator fish, or a photographer, can scare the worm into retracting into its tube, instantly.

*Right: The hard coral
Dendrophyllia gracilis
dominates the northern vertical
faces of the reef. In daylight the
yellow polyps are often fully
retracted into their polyp cups.*

*Below and far right: A delicate
polyp of Dendrophyllia with its
fully extended tentacles. This coral
is a voracious feeder which catches
small planktonic animals, and
literally stuffs them into their
central mouths.*

Below: Known as the Christmas tree worm, Spirobranchus giganteus, is distinctive in having two branches of spiralling, feeding tentacles which emerge from a calcareous tube. This tube is often buried deep within the coral, and when disturbed, the worm retreats inside, plugging it with a lid (or operculum) seen at the bottom of this photograph.

Right: A colony of Spirobranchus giganteus found on a coral head at South Point. The reasons for such a diversity of colouration are unclear, however, it would appear that each worm can produce offspring of different colours. The colony is easily panicked into retracting by the slightest movement, where a spike protects the tube's opening.

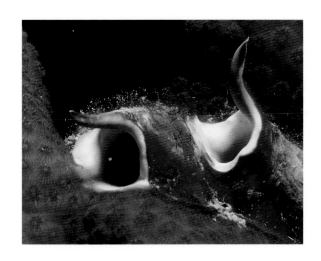

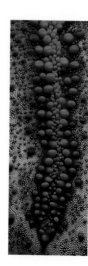

*C*areful observation and research will always reward the diver with a spectacular array of creatures in this highly biodiversified environment.

Starfish in various segmented forms vie for space on the reef with tiny armoured shrimps, aggressive crabs and lobsters.

Molluscs found at Sipadan are a living example of the evolution of this species; originally shell carriers, some have cast off protective casings to evolve alternate forms.

The nudibranch displays a wide range of spectacular colours, while the intelligent octopus is a master of concealment.

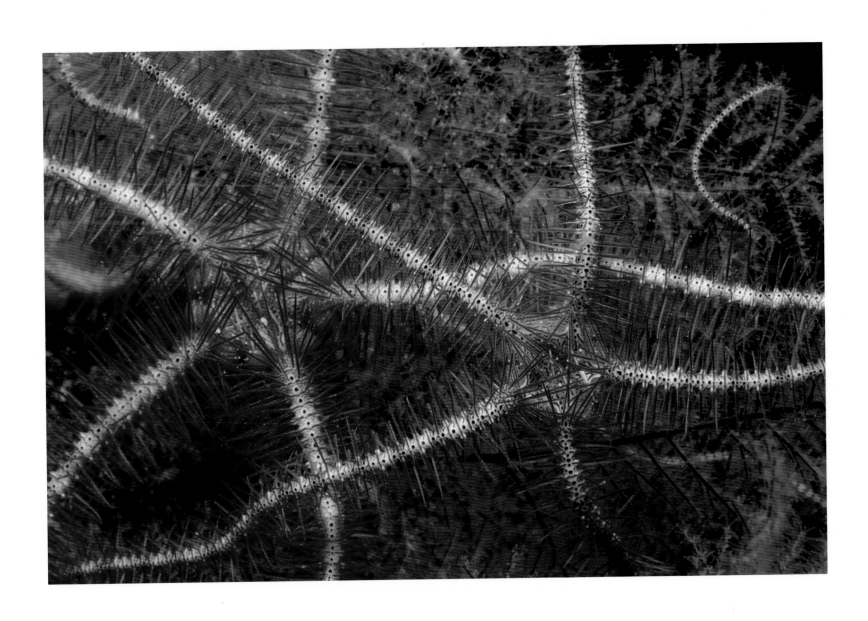

Preceding page: The delicate spiny brittle star, Ophiothrix purpurea, *is found on the reef during daylight, unlike other species which hide themselves. It inhabits the sponges, soft coral and gorgonian coral and is thought to feed on particles suspended in the water.*

Far left: In addition to the ability to grow new limbs, some starfish can grow a completely new creature from a single part in a matter of weeks. Here, Linckia multifora, *is in the process of regenerating a new body from a single arm.*

Left and below: The most destructive creature on the reef is the Crown of Thorns starfish, Acanthaster planci, *which is responsible for the death of huge areas of coral reefs worldwide. It eats the living coral by sucking out the polyps from inside the limestone crust, turning it from its usual green or brown to deathly white. Fortunately at Sipadan, I have only come across this species twice. The spines are sharp and should the diver be pierced, infection will result.*

Below: Snuggling up to a sand covered sea cucumber, Holothuria, the cushion star, Choriaster granulatus, has small "gills" protruding through its smooth skin giving it a granular appearance. It feeds on coral polyps and small invertebrates.

Right: A large pin-cushion star, Culcita novaeguineae, sits on the edge of the reef drop-off. With the potential of growing to 20 centimetres in diameter, this characteristic star feeds on the living coral, detritus and micro-organism films on the reef.

Left : Close-up views of the feathery arms of crinoids reveal an efficient mesh that sieves particulate food materials from the water.

Right: In slack water the feather star, Comanthus bennetti, *relaxes its position. During periods of current flow, the star spreads its arms in a fan shape across the current presenting a maximum surface area to trap food particles.*

Below: The shrimp
Periclimenes longicarpus,
adopts its host's colouration for
protection, to live in symbiosis
with the cushion starfish.

Right: A related and strikingly
patterned shrimp, the Periclimenes
brevicarpalis *lives in close*
association with the carpet anemone,
Cryptodendrum.

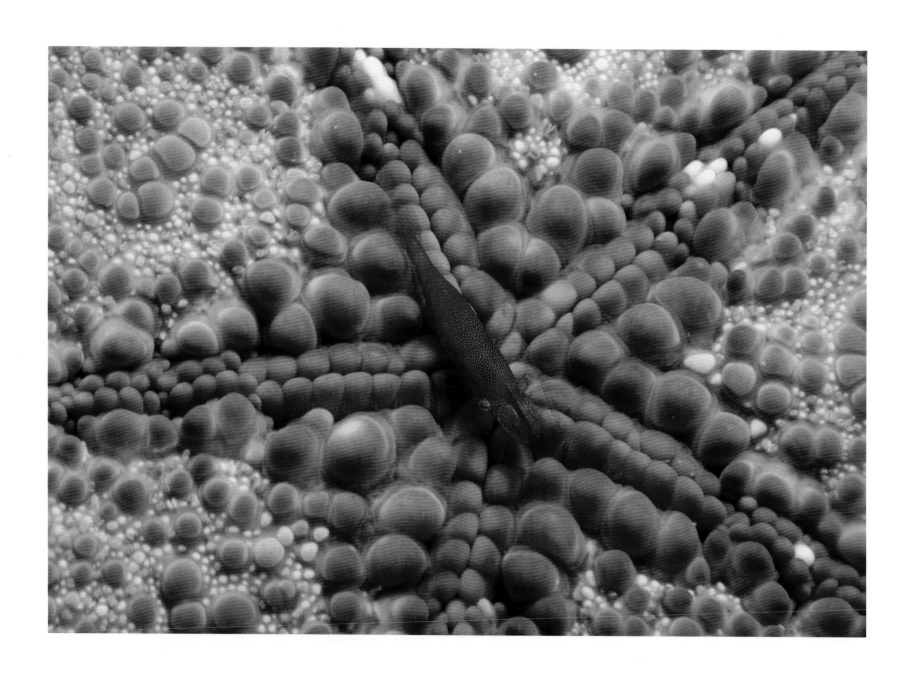

Left: The Periclimenes shrimp species are well camouflaged for protection. Here three shrimps merge with their sponge host.

Below: Shy, and hard to find, two small Periclimenes shrimps are discovered in a gap between the spheres of the Plerogyra, *bubble coral.*

Below: The shrimp, Periclimenes holthuisi, *is translucent with small dark patches on its body and banding on the legs as can be seen when the creature is placed on a uniform background, such as a sponge.*

The eyes and sensitive antennae are large in comparison to the body of this small creature.

Right: The distinctive banded coral shrimp, Stenopus hispidus, *commonly feeds on the external parasites of fish providing a mutually beneficial service. The waving of its long white antennae attracts the fish to the "cleaning station", where they remain passive during the shrimp's feeding period.*

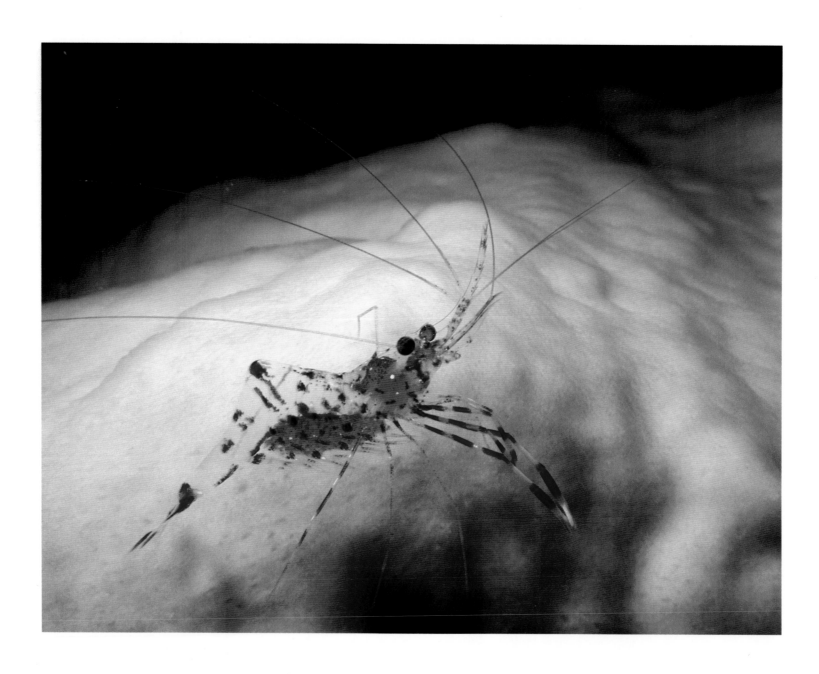

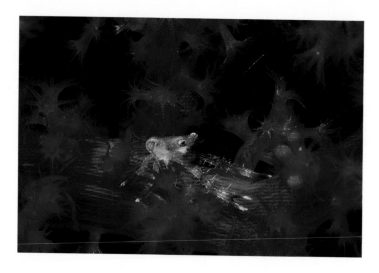

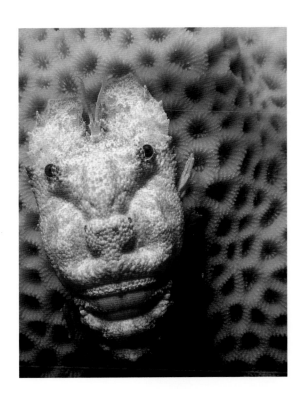

Far left: A small squat lobster, Galathea, adopts a dramatically lit defensive posture amongst the arms of a feather star.

Far left, below: Concealed amongst the vivid red polyps of the soft coral is a small transparent galatheid crab. When approached, it waves its long pincer armed legs defensively.

Left: Seen from this angle, the bizzare-looking slipper lobster, Scyllarides haani, hunts the reef for bivalves.

Below: The painted lobster (or crayfish) Panulirus versicolor, is the largest species of crustacean found on coral reef.
At night the colonies leave their hiding places at Lobster Lair to forage for food in hunting grounds which can cover several kilometres.

Left: Scavenging for food amongst the coral is the red shiny crab, Carpilius corallinus. Smaller relatives of this crustacean can frequently be found living inside large basket sponges.

Far left, below: The tiny crab, Trapezia, is an obligate associate of the cauliflower coral, Pocillopora damicornis. It can only be found on this coral and will not leave the coral even when threatened by danger.

Left, below: This small crab lives in association with sponges and adopts the same colour as the sponge for effective camouflage.

Below: The tiny spotted anemone crab, Neopetrolisthes ohshimai, grows to a mere 1-2 centimetres in diameter, and lives amongst the tentacles of giant anemones. Paired couples of male and female crabs inhabit a single anemone, and are immune to the stings of their host.

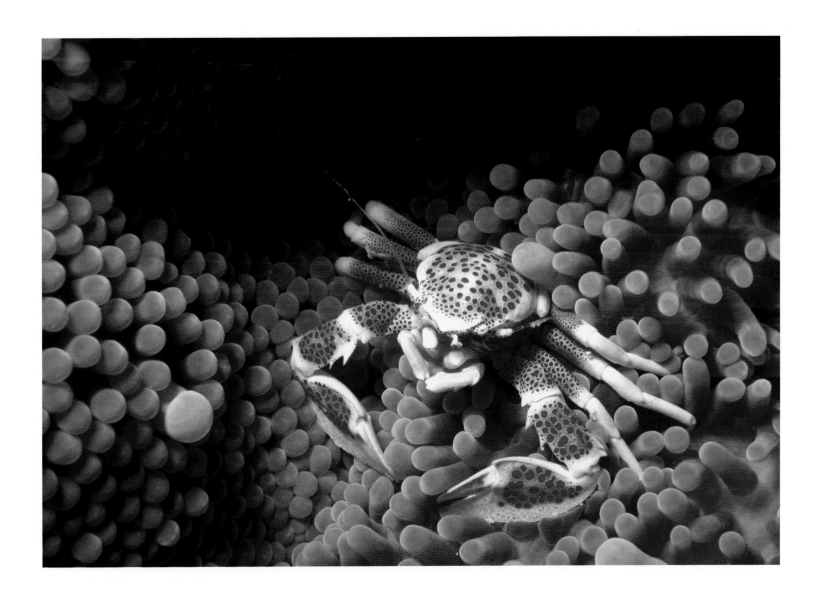

Below: Inhabiting the soft coral, the highly decorative white spider crab, Macropodia, *is slow moving, and although usually well camouflaged, it can be revealed by the camera's flash.*

Right: The large hermit crab, Aniculus maximus, *has bristles at the front and on its golden yellow legs for added protection. A fearsome predator, this crab snaps at any creature in the range of its powerful claws.*

Right, below: One of the largest of the hermit crab species, Dardanus megistos, *casually strolls over the coral rubble. Empty shells are often collected by visitors to the sea side, thus depriving a growing hermit crab of a home.*

Decorator crabs, of the Majidae family, cover their bodies with sponges and other animals to provide camouflage. It is only when they move from their hiding place that they can be seen.

*Below: The predatory cone shell,
Conus geographus, actively
seeks its food at night. It uses its
extended siphon to test the water
for the scent of its potential victim,
usually another mollusc.
Its venomous sting can be
dangerous to man, as well as its
intended prey.*

*Right: The variegated tun shell,
Tonna variegata, burrows into
sandy areas using its large broad
foot, and feeds on sea cucumbers
which have few natural predators.*

Left: The spotted glossy shell of the tiger cowry, Cypraea tigris, is covered by a fleshy mantle when grazing on reef algae at night.

Below: A small cowry, Calpurnus sp., is well camouflaged amongst the red branches of soft coral.

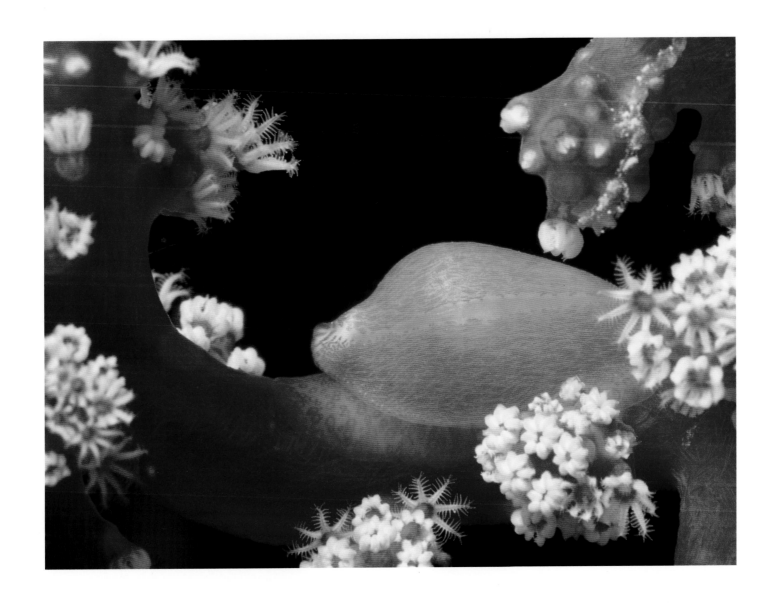

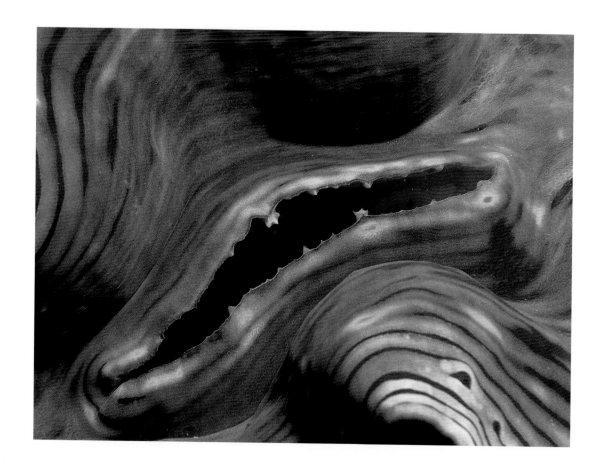

Left: The Tridacna clam is a filter feeder, drawing in nutrient rich water through an opening in its mantle (here seen in close up). Microscopic organisms are caught in its internal filter while the water is expelled from exhalent opening (below).

Right: Growing in symbiosis with giant clams, Tridacna, oxygen producing algae lends colour to the mantle of this harmless creature.

Below: Only one centimetre in diameter, the beautiful, file shell, Promantellem vigens, normally lives on sand beneath coral rubble. When disturbed, this tiny creature proves itself to be an excellent swimmer. The spectacular retractable tentacles around the edge of its mantle are taste organs.

Right: Fused to the coral, the thorny oyster, Spondylus aurantius, sits feeding with its shell open showing its gills behind the mantle. These gills filter food particles from the current flowing through.

Right, below: Playing host to a bright red sponge, Microciona, the zig-zag edge of the shell of the cocks-comb oyster, Lopha cristagalli, can be seen clearly.

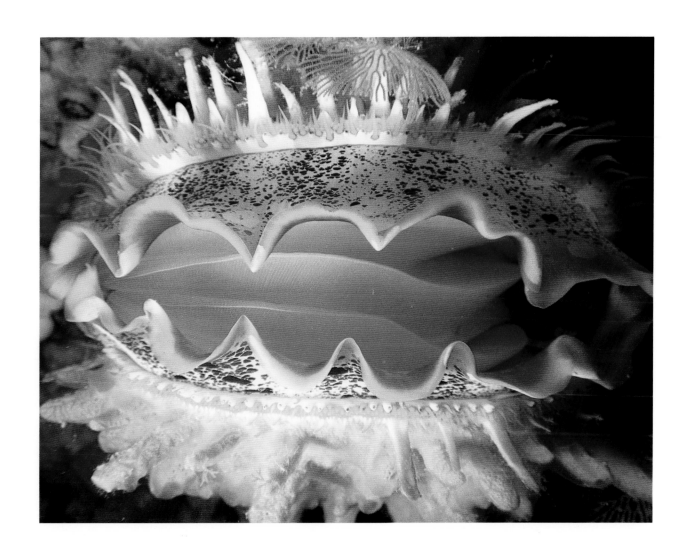

Below: Often called the orchids of the ocean, the nudibranch (naked gills) can be found in all parts of the world from arctic waters to tropical mangrove swamps. These carnivorous, hermaphrodite sea-slugs often have foul tasting, venomous glands in their skin, and are brightly coloured to deter predators.

A common sight at Sipadan is the pyjama nudibranch, Chromodoris quadricolor.

Right: The lilac and white Chromodoris bullocki *has a large tuft of gills at the posterior end of its body.*

Left, top: The brightly spotted Dendrodoris *even has spots on its tentacles, while its characteristic naked gills are easily identifiable.*

Left: Calmella *collects the cells of its stinging coral prey, storing them in leaf-like processes on the body to be used for defence.*

Left, bottom: Related to the warty Phyllidia, *this nudibranch has characteristic feather-like tentacles.*

Right: Casella, *which feeds on sponges, is a striking nudibranch with a fringe surrounding its leathery body.*

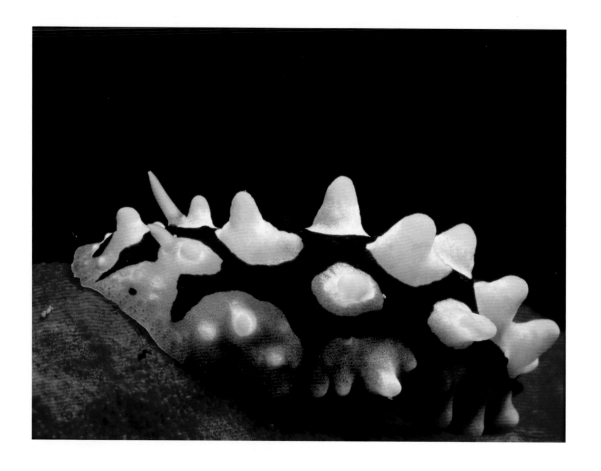

Above: The wart-like protuberances and strong colouration are characteristic of the Phyllidia varicosa, nudibranch, which exudes a toxic mucus from its skin to repel predators.

Left: The yellow nudibranch, Notodoris minor, grow to a length of 10 centimetres and lay gelatinous ribbons of yellow eggs. The eggs are abandoned by the parent immediately they are laid.

Right: Pleurobranchus species are soft bodied molluscs which have lost their shell. It has a long feathery gill on the right side between the foot and mantle. Many of this species secrete a strong acid to repel predators.

A fast moving hunter of fish and crustaceans, this cuttle fish, Sepia pharaonis, was spotted off Barracuda Point. Just under one metre in length this species has the ability to change colour to match its habitat, as can be seen in these three pictures of a single individual.

The reef squid, Sepioteuthis rivals fish in its ability to swim. With delicately pigmented skin cells it has the remarkable ability to change colour. This squid possesses two modified tentacles that can be rapidly shot out at its prey. The suckers at the tip can fix to even the fastest of fish, and its eyes are almost mammal-like in their development.

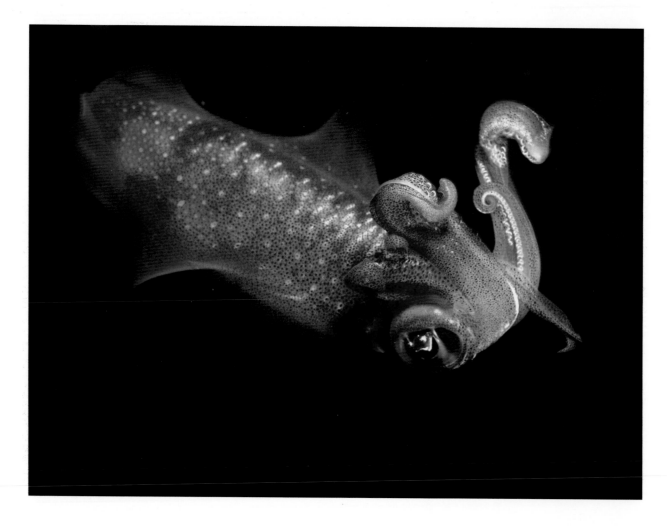

Right: In daylight, Octopus cyaneus hides, concealed in its lair where it keeps a wary eye on the movements of the diver. When in danger, octopus, cuttle fish and squid squirt ink to cover their escape.

Below: The octopus emerges from its lair at night to feed on shrimps, crabs and small fish with its sharp beak. Highly intelligent creatures, it uses its tentacles to crawl over the reef, but is also capable of bursts of jet-propelled speed swimming.

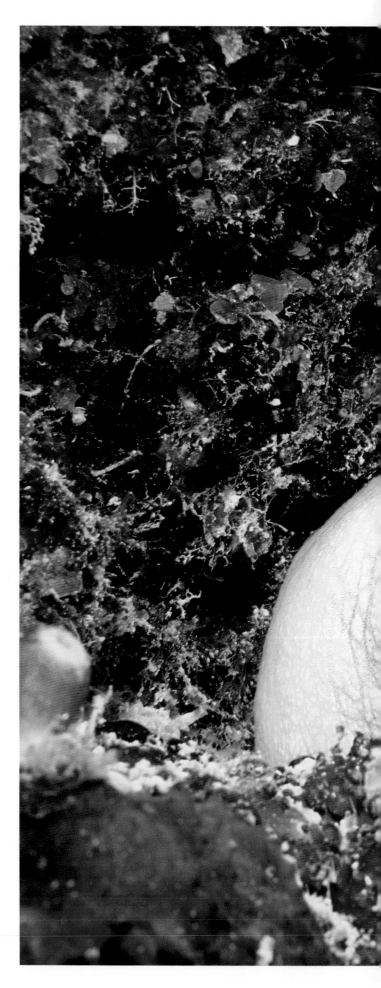

*S*ipadan is unique in Malaysian waters in

that it provides feeding and breeding grounds

for both tiny reef fish and huge oceanic species.

Camouflage and colour also play a role in

their survival. The leaf fish sways in the

current perfectly disguised, while the lion

fish with its venomous spines and brightly

coloured feather-like fins warns off species

rash enough to consider it as prey.

Part of the Sipadan experience is the

great numbers of schooling fish to be found

swimming in tight packs for protection,

mating and feeding. Shoaling manta rays,

barracuda and hammerhead sharks, all oceanic

species, can be found in the strong currents

at the north-east of the island.

Preceding page, below and right:
Schools of Sphyraena
barracuda *inhabit the Sipadan*
reef off South Point as well as at
the aptly named Barracuda Point.
Thousands of these metre long fish
swim in tight circles offering divers
an awesome sight.
The barracuda is often miscast as
one of the most feared predatory
fish. However, the species at
Sipadan are, as far as humans are
concerned, docile and unconcerned
with divers invading their territory.

Left: Catching the sun's rays is a shoal of tuna fish of the Thunnus species. Swimming at speed, the tuna preys on other fish species, squid and crustaceans. A prized catch by the world's fishing fleets, the tuna is commercially harvested, perilously close to Sipadan's waters.

Below: Out of the blue swim a small shoal of silver pompano, Trachinotus blochii, which feeds on small fish living in the surface waters or near reefs.

An encounter with a shoal of hammerhead sharks, Sphyrna zygaena, *is a unique experience for any diver. Over a period of ten days there were persistent reports of sightings of this rare phenomenon in the strong currents off Barracuda Point at about 65 metres. However my chance encounter with the submarine pack lasted less than five seconds - just long enough to take one single photograph.*

Above: The grey shark, Carcharinus amblyrhyncos, is a common inhabitant of an amphitheatre area at Barracuda Point. An aggressive or curious creature at depths of more than 65 metres, this three metre long predator can charge at divers with apparently murderous intent, only to veer off in the last four metres of their supposed attack.

To most people the shark is the most feared of all of the sea creatures. However, to the diving fraternity, the shark is usually regarded as shy and harmless, and only dangerous when their feeding territory is invaded or when provoked. Divers should, however, never underestimate the shark's potential for aggression.

Right, above: Nurse shark, Nebrius ferrugineus.

Right: Leopard shark, Stegostoma fasciatum.

Far right: White tipped reef shark, Triaenodon obesus.

Another of Sipadan's rare sights is a shoal of manta rays, Manta birostris, 'flying' in bomber formation over Barracuda Point. They can grow to a wingspan of up to seven metres and weigh up to three tons. The manta feeds on nothing larger than shrimps.

Below: Also known as devil fish, obviously as a result of their appearance, they are the most primitive of all vertebrates.

Right: From below, the head fins can be seen in the characteristic feeding position, while the ten slits containing the gills are also visible. These gentle giants have few enemies other than the killer whale, Orca, or some shark species. This particular individual has experienced a close encounter of the shark kind.

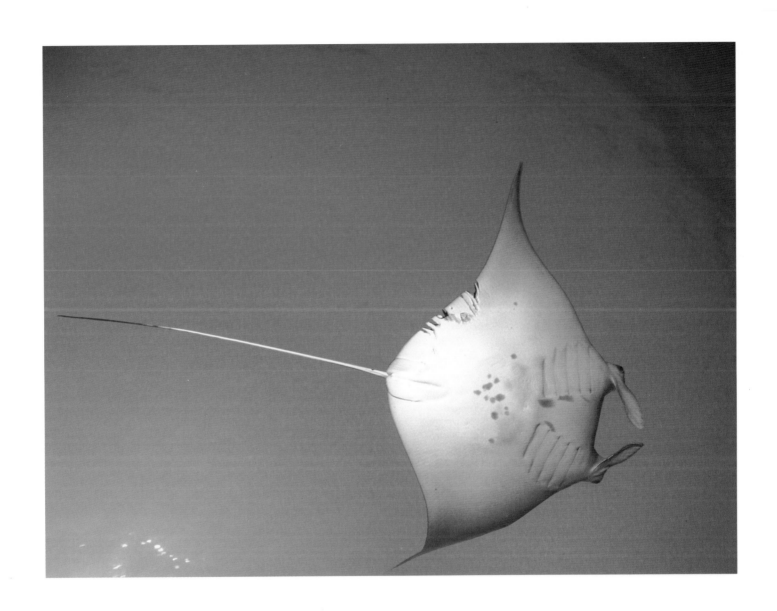

Left: Swimming gracefully past the Sipadan reef, the spotted eagle ray, Aetobatus narinari, *feeds on molluscs and crustaceans which it collects from the sandy sea bed.*

Below: Uncommon at Sipadan, the electric ray, Torpedo marmorata, *generates an electric shock which it sends out into the water, either to stun its prey, or to ward off predators.*

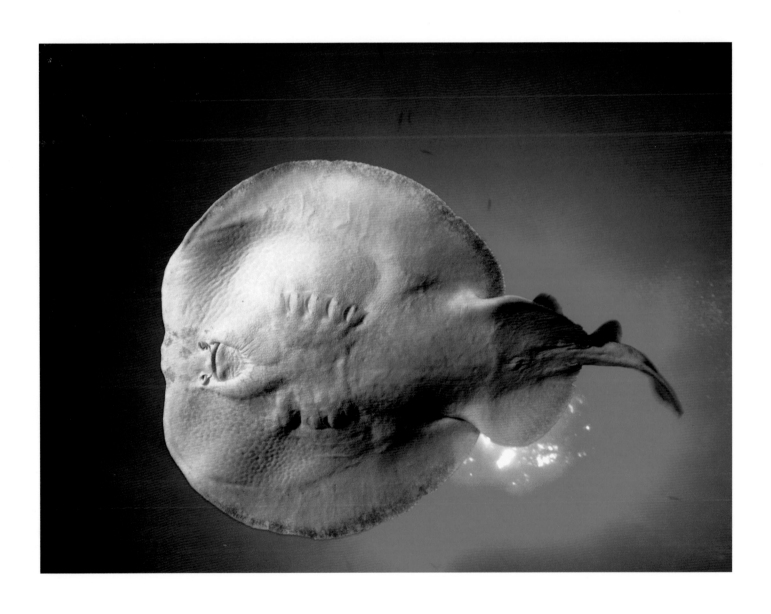

Above: A pair of black-spotted sting rays, Taeniura melanospila, *pirouette along the edge of the reef. As one of the largest of the bottom dwelling rays, it can grow to widths of two metres, while its tail contains a sharp spike which it can curl over its body to protect its head from attack.*

Right: The blue-spotted sting ray, Taeniura lymma, *is usually seen digging out molluscs and worms from the coral rubble or sand at the base of the reef.*

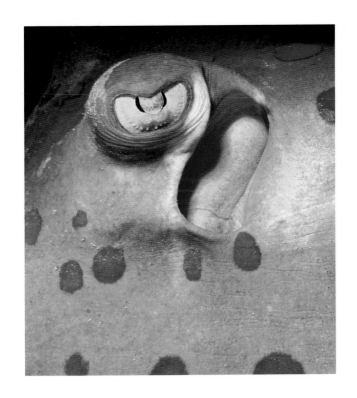

Left: An explosion of anchovies shoaling in the open water.

Below: Circling in the sunlit water the surgeon fish, Acanthurus, is so called because of the two lancets, one on either side near the base of the tail fin, which can cut as cleanly as a scalpel.

Left: Found in large schools during daylight hours the yellow back fusilier, Caesio teres, feed on planktonic animals in mid water over the reef, and are particularly abundant along the steep outer slopes of the reef.

Below: Caesio xanthonotus sweep low over the reef in fast moving schools.

Left: Hovering over the reef near the jetty, a shoal of yellow fin goat fish, Mulloides vanicolensis, disperse at night to feed on sand-dwelling creatures such as worms by raking the sand with the long barbels under their chin.

Below: A group of long-fin banner fish, Heniochus acuminatus, follow the sun's rays down through the water to deeper layers in search of the minute animals and algae on which they feed.

Commonly found on the northern parts of the island the bigeye trevally, Caranx sexfasciatus, are very friendly towards divers. Powerful swimmers, they school to depths of 100 metres and feed on smaller fish and crustaceans mainly at night.

Left: Illuminated by the sun, the longfin bat fish, Platax teira, is distinctive for its continuous dorsal fin and yellow pelvic fan.

Right, above: Two juvenile bat fish capture the magic of the underwater world.

Right, below: A small school of bat fish swimming slowly over the reef.

Above: A typical schooling formation of more than 60 humphead parrot fish, Bolbometopon muricatum, with the characteristic hump clearly distinguishable in these silhouetted forms.

With the morning sun's rays the humpheads congregate at Barracuda Point, the shoal then moves off around the island in search of food. At night they retire to the northern area around the drop-off where they can be found sleeping in shallow depths at around two metres.

Right: The giant parrot fish can easily reach lengths of over a metre and weigh up to 75 kilogrammes, and is reputed to use its hump to ram the coral on which it feeds.

Left: Inside the entrance chamber of Turtle Cavern the squirrel fish, Myripristis vittatus, *can also be found in the dark crevices around the reef. It is noted for the sound it produces by vibrating the muscles attached to its swim-bladder. On occasion, this sound may even be heard above the surface of the water and is used to advertise territorial occupation or as a mating call.*

Below: The big-eye, Priacanthus hamrur, *remains under overhangs, or close to the coral during the day, emerging at night to feed on small crabs, squid or other fish.*

Above: The spotted unicorn fish,
Naso brevirostris, *swims lazily
through the water. A daylight
feeding species, it returns to the reef
for shelter at night.*

Left: A dramatic view of the file
fish, Aluterus monoceros, *which
is a rare sight on the coral reef.*

Below and far left: An inflated porcupine fish, Chilomycterus spilostyus, *which has the ability to inflate itself as a protection against predators such as sharks which have been known to choke to death whilst attempting to eat them. Their hard beak-like jaws easily crush the shells of molluscs and sea urchins on which they feed.*

Left: Another variety of porcupine fish, Diodon liturosus, *or short spined porcupine fish is distinctively coloured.*

Below: The puffer fish, Arothron stellatus, permanently guards the entrance to Turtle Cavern.

Right: The black-spotted puffer fish, Arothron nigropunctatus, nestles amongst the branches of a sea fan. It is a common sight wherever there is an abundance of live coral, in particular the Acropora, on which it feeds.

Right, below: A deformed puffer fish, Arothron nigropunctatus.

The boxfish, Ostracion cubicus, are from the same species although background colouration varies. The boxfish is heavily armoured for protection, resulting in a stiff body which requires it to move slowly.

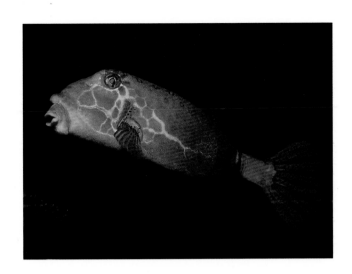

Left: The fan like pectoral fins are characteristic of the zebra lion fish, Dendrochirus zebra, *seen here resting on the coral rubble. The female of the species is much smaller and more aggressive than the male and develops a pale white face when ready to spawn.*

Left, below: The majestic lion fish, Pterois volitans, *with its enlarged pectoral fins and elongated dorsal fin spines, is one of the more spectacular inhabitants of the reef. The spines can inflict painful wounds when the fish is harassed.*

Below: A lion fish yawns, bored with the photo session.

Above: A portrait of the tasseled scorpion fish, Scorpaena oxycephala, *showing the numerous flaps and tassels on the face and under the chin. Its large upturned mouth engulfs any small fish which swims past.*

Right: The scorpion fish varies in colouration to blend with the environment.

Left: Hidden amongst the coral rubble, the ugly warty stone fish, Synanceia verrucosa, *waits for its prey. The stone fish can inflict a painful wound with its venomous spines.*

A member of the scorpion fish family, the leaf fish, Taenianotus triacanthus, comes in a variety of colours from black to white. Hard to find on the seabed and resting amongst the coral, this 75 millimetre long fish sways in the current and resembles natural vegetation.

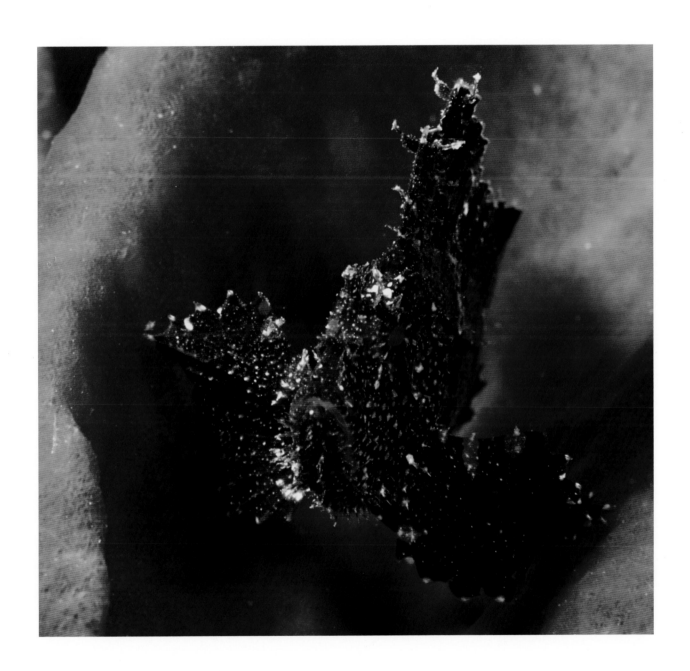

*Restricted to the Indo Pacific
reefs, the genus Pseudanthias.
These shoaling fairy basslet feed
in mid water and are socially
structured into harems
comprising one dominant male
and a large number of females.
Should the male dies, the most
dominant female will undergo a
sex change to lead the shoal.*

*Below: Purple yellow-striped
fairy basslet Pseudanthias
tuka.*

*Right, clockwise: Peach fairy
basslet, Pseudanthias dispar.
Male fairy basslet,
Pseudanthias squamippinus.
Male square spot fairy basslet,
Pseudanthias pleurotaenia.
Male red cheeked fairy basslet
Pseudanthias huchti with a
greatly developed third dorsal
spine. The red cheek band does
not appear in females.*

Left: The sabre-toothed blenny, Plagiotremus rhynorhynchus, with prominent blue streaks along its body, peers warily out from the coral hole in which it is living. The blenny feeds by darting out to bite off pieces of skin and scales from other passing fish.

Above: It varies in colour from yellow-brown to black, and, in its black phase mimics the cleaner wrasse, Labroides dimidiatus, to deceive larger fish into believing that it is a cleaning species.

Left: This colourful hawk fish, Cirrhitichthys falco, is a small grouper-like fish which waits at the base of coral heads for its prey. A territorial species, the males appear to have a harem of females.

Below: The longnose hawk fish, Oxycirrhites typus, normally lives amongst the branches of sea fans or soft coral where the body profile is broken up by its patterns and is rarely seen in the company of others.

Left: Longnose file fish, Oxymonacanthus longirostris, *with its blue yellow-spotted body is found with the coral* Acropora, *on which it feeds exclusively, using its pointed snout to pick polyps from their coral cups.*

Below: The long dorsal and anal fins are characteristic of the fire goby, Nemateleotris magnifica. *The fire goby is easily scared by passing divers, and rapidly burrows in the sand should it be startled.*

Above: This small goby peers out from colonies of the ascidian, Didemnum molle, *where it seeks refuge.*

Right: Goby, Amblyelotris wheeleri, *a common sight on reefs throughout the region, this species lives in symbiosis with the shrimp.*

Below: The minute goby, Eviota sp., rarely grows to more than 25 millimetres in length and makes a striking contrast against the plate coral, the globe of bubble coral (right), and in close up resting on a branch of whip coral (bottom right).

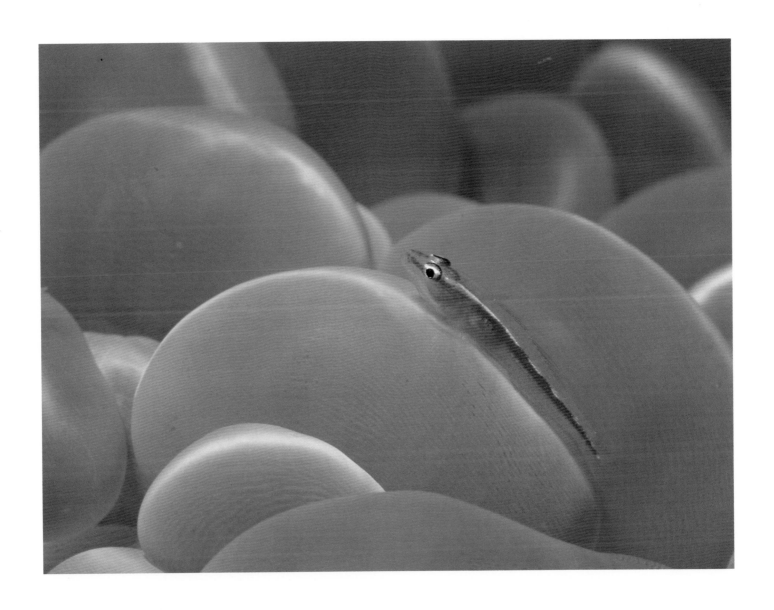

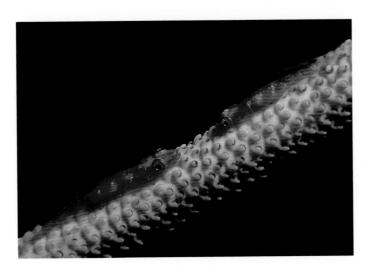

Below: The cleaner wrasse here cleans the back of the sweetlips, Plectorhinchus lineatus. Like all cleaner fish the wrasse performs a mutually beneficial service for many species of fish. By establishing a territory called a cleaning station, they create a sort of neutral zone where all manner of fish come in a trance-like truce to have the parasites cleaned from their bodies and inside their mouths and gills, by the cleaners, as in the case of this Plectorhinchus picus (far right).

Right: These cleaner wrasses, Labroides dimidiatus, are apparently kissing each other. The most common fish cleaner in the region, the wrasse hides at night in small holes in the reef, often secreting a mucus cocoon around itself.

Left: The largest of the species, the long-jawed squirrel fish, Sargocentron spiniferum, usually hides in caves or under ledges during the day emerging at night to feed.

Below: The coral grouper, Cephalopholis miniata, with its blue spots on a red background is one of the most beautiful of coral reef fish. It can be found at considerable depths, down as deep as 150 metres.

Below: The parrot-fish, Scarus psittacus, with its large beak is an obvious reef fish, which grazes mainly on the film of algae growing on coral rock. At night it sleeps by wrapping itself in a mucus cocoon which may help stop its scent from reaching possible predators, such as moray eels.

Right , below: This parrot fish is safe inside its cocoon, while a small red and white banded shrimp attempts to penetrate it.

Right: Topped by a moustache of algae the front teeth of the parrot fish are regenerative, while it also possesses another set of grinding teeth in its throat.

Far right: Characteristic of a visit from a parrot fish the coral displays scrape marks in the covering of algae.

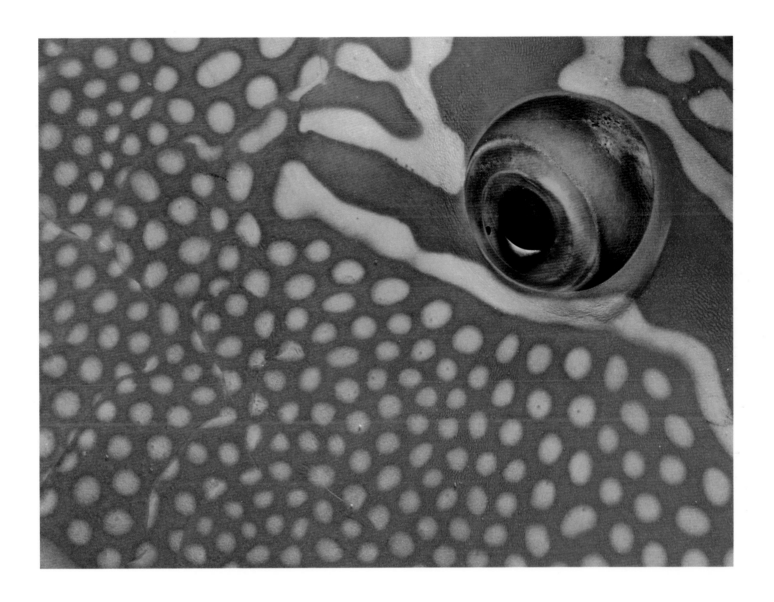

Strikingly coloured the Sipadan parrot fish can be found in a wide variety of patterns. Even the detail of their eyes displays spectacular colouration.

Below: The head and stalked bright eyes of the peacock flounder, Bothus lunatus. *This creature's body sports a blue-spotted pattern, but on the sandy bottom it always appears well camouflaged.*

Right: The crocodile fish, Cociella crocodila, *is a master of disguise, and is so called because of its resemblance to the crocodile.*

Right, below: A detail of the eye of the crocodile fish showing the characteristic iris lapel, a branched tassel-like structure which hangs over the eye. This can expand over it's eye to shade from excessive sunlight or camouflage it from prospective prey.

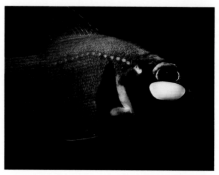  

Left, clockwise: Inside the limestone caverns living in the darkness, the flashlight fish, Photoblepharon palpebratus, has a cream coloured patch under each eye containing a colony of luminescent bacteria which live in symbiosis with the fish. The light from the bacteria attracts prey, and allows communication with the rest of the school.
The eye has a special lid which can cover the bacteria patch to give a flashing-light effect.

Right: A member of the seahorse family, Solenostomus cyanopterus resembles a dead leaf of sea grass waving in the current.

Sipadan has at least nine varieties of the anemone (or clown) fish, Amphiprion species. These fish live as mated pairs amongst the tentacles of large sea anemones which provide protection. Socially structured in female dominated pairs, their lifestyle is so well adapted that the male has the ability to change sex should a female die.

Below: Amphiprion rubrocintus.

Right: Although the anemone has venomous tentacles, the Amphiprion is covered in a film of mucus to protect against the venomous stings of its host. Here, an Amphiprion clarkii snuggles into its anemone host.

*Clown fish usually spawn during
full moon, laying eggs at the
base of the anemone, and are
looked after by the male of the pair.*

Below: Amphiprion ocellaris.

*The anemone fish is also known as
clown fish, because of its facial
white striping which resembles a
clown's make-up.*

Right, top: Amphiprion
sandaracinos.

Right, centre: Premnas
biaculeatus.

Right, bottom: Amphiprion
perideraion.

Found at West Ridge, a nest of the highly venomous juvenile cat fish, Plotosus lineatus.

Left: Thought to be the world's largest (but not longest) moray eel, the giant moray, Gymnothorax javanicus, can reach weights of up to 35 kilogrammes with a body width of up to 0.5 metre across. Although they look fierce, they are relatively docile, attacking only when provoked.

Left, below: The white spotted face of Gymnothorax tesselata.

Below: Head of Gymnothorax sp. showing the large eye and sharp teeth.

Left: The spotted garden eel,
Heteroconger hassi, *lives in a
tube in the sand into which it
burrows with its tail.*

*Above: Colonising areas of the sea
bed they congregate in garden like
formations waving in the current.
When danger threatens they
retract into their burrows.*

Far left: The peppered moray,
Siderea picta, *lacks the large
fangs of the* Gymnothorax *and
feeds on crustaceans.*

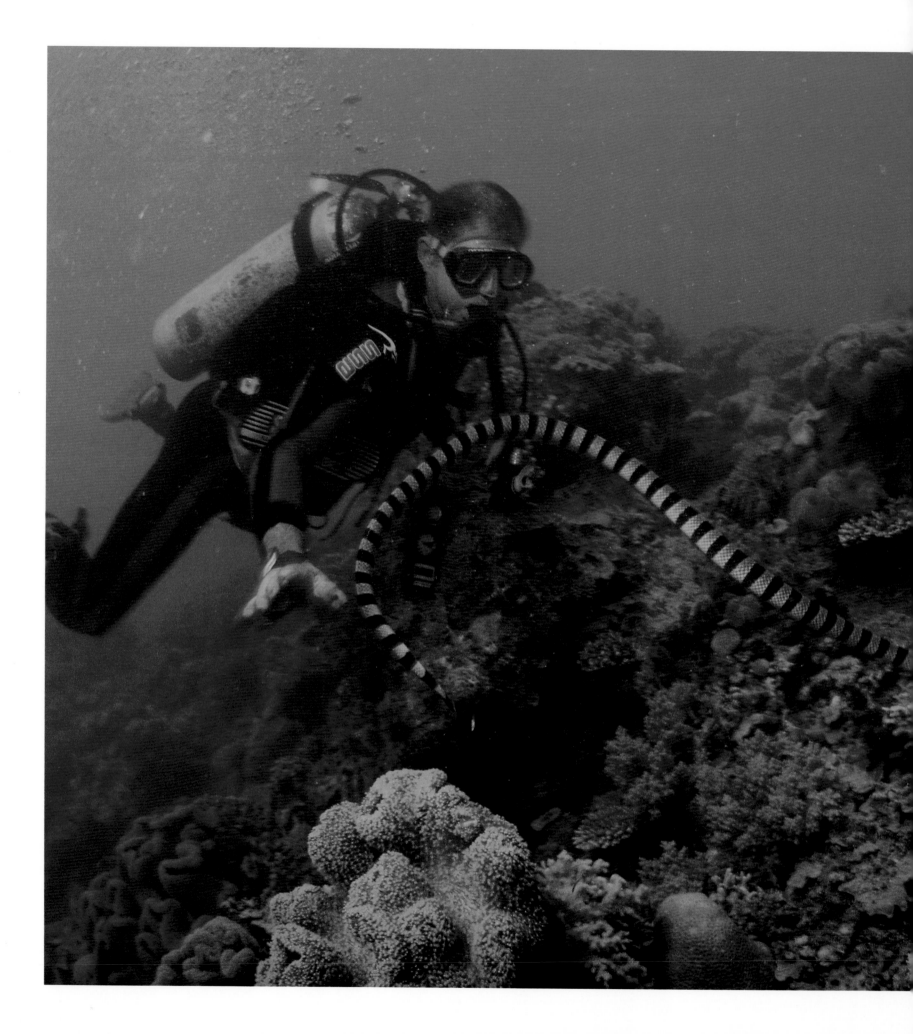

Above: Air breathing, the sea krait must regularly swim to the surface.

Left: Of all of the sea snakes, the yellow-lipped sea krait, Laticauda colubrina, *is the least dependent on the marine environment. Highly venomous despite its very small mouth, it spends much of its time on land laying eggs and sunning itself. It ventures into the sea to feed propelling itself with its flattened rudder shaped tail.*
This female specimen is 1.5 metres in length, males generally only grow to half this size.

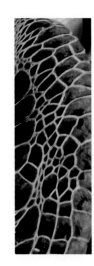

*T*he sheer numbers of docile turtles found in the Sipadan waters have astounded scientists and amateur divers alike. Although sea turtles are an endangered species, I have encounterd upwards of thirty of these delightful creatures in a single dive, particularly during the October mating season.

Marine turtles can be observed mating, feeding and resting on ledges oblivious to the watching humans.

For the diver, Turtle Tomb is the saddest of all the underwater experiences at Sipadan, and only rarely are visitors escorted into the maze of caverns which lead to the tomb chamber.

Preceding page: Turtles can often be observed mating at Sipadan. However, during the peak season of October, groups of six or more green turtles can be found coupling.

Above: Friendly creatures, turtles are air breathers, and periodically return to the surface. This green turtle appears to be saluting an old friend.

Right, above: When the turtle is asleep it is most vulnerable. To avoid startling the animals, divers should be careful not to approach too near a sleeping turtle.

Right: A portrait of the green turtle.

Left: By the Drop Off a school of rainbow runners, Elagatis bipinnulata, escort a green turtle.

Below: Remora sucker fish, Echeneis naucrates, can frequently be seen attached to turtles at Sipadan.

Right, above: At the cleaning station at South Point, a green turtle floats motionless while having the algae removed from its shell by surgeon fish, Acanthurus.

Right, below: On a coral head, two female green turtles have a rest.

Left: The sex of an adult turtle can be distinguished by the size of its tail. The male has a long tail, while that of the female is very short.

Above: Trapped by one fin in a crevasse in the reef at South point, this poor creature drowned. When this photograph was taken, scavengers had only begun to eat the eyes.

Right: Two days later while diving on the same spot, I discovered that the entire carcass had been picked clean, leaving only the skeleton and shell .

*Below and right, below: An
endangered species marine turtles
are plentiful around Sipadan.
The hawksbill, Eretmochelys
imbricata, is in particular danger
since its beautiful shell is in great
demand commercially.*

*Right: Oblivious to the diver's
camera, the hawksbill burrows into
the seabed with its beak to feed.*

*Far right: Sponges are a favourite
dessert for the hawksbill.*

Left: Thirty metres down, a spectacular black coral bush, Antipathes, more than two metres high guards the entrance to Turtle Cavern.

Below: Two divers approach the elliptical entrance to Turtle Cavern.

Left: While the ceiling inside Turtle Cavern is clean, remnants of an early strata of limestone rock covered in marine growth jut out into the flow.

Right: In a side passage, bubbles generated by divers form lenses trapped on the cavern's ceiling.

Below: An indication that the cavern was once above the surface, a stalactite created in a dry cave, has been eroded by the tidal swell of the ocean.

Left: An interconnecting passage between two chambers.

Right: An abandoned passage inside the cavern's interconnected labyrinth, with a deposit of fine white sand on the floor, and steps eroded by water.

Known as Turtle Tomb, the romantic view is that turtles have made these underwater caverns their graveyard. The fact is even sadder for these creatures. Once inside the dark limestone labyrinth of passages and chambers, the turtles easily lose their way out and drown.